Snollygoster
and other poems
HELEN DUNMORE

D1580661

SCHOLASTIC
PRESS

Scholastic Children's Books,
Commonwealth House, 1-19 New Oxford Street,
London, WC1A 1NU, UK
a division of Scholastic Ltd
London ~ New York ~ Toronto ~ Sydney ~ Auckland
Mexico City ~ New Delhi ~ Hong Kong

First published in the UK by Scholastic Ltd, 2001

ISBN 0 439 99636 8

Printed at Mackays of Chatham Ltd.

10 9 8 7 6 5 4 3 2 1

contents

over the green hill

Two boys, a girl in a red coat,
a leaping, dancing, spring-mad dog
fighting its leash, released
to run like water over the hill
the green hill, with mystery running after.

Where are they going and why so happy,
why the red flag of her coat flapping
like poppy-silk against the green,
why are they all running
like water over the top of the hill,
the green hill, with secrets running after?

What is the country they are running to,
is there peace there, is there freedom
to jump and play in the spring air,
why are they all running, why do they look
behind them, and laugh, and run faster,
why are they holding hands as they run
over that green hill with the wind running after?

smiles like roses

All down my street
smiles opened like roses
sun licked me and tickled me
sun said, Didn't you believe me
when I said I'd be back?

I blinked my eyes, I said,
Sun, you are too strong for me
where'd you get those muscles?
Sun said, Come and dance.

All over the park
smiles opened like roses
babies kicked off their shoes
and sun kissed their toes.

All those new babies
all that new sun
everybody dancing
walking but dancing.

All over the world
sun kicked off his shoes
and came home dancing
licking and tickling

kissing crossing-ladies and fat babies
saying to everyone
Hey you are the most beautiful
dancing people I've ever seen
with those smiles like roses!

yellow

Think of something yellow.

The sun?
A fat ripe pear
or buttercup petals?

Yellow is butter.
Yellow is custard.
Yellow is egg-yolks.

Yellow has all the answers.
Yellow is like
an advert that twists your eyes
till they light on yellow.

What is yellow?

Nobody answered.
Shakeela smiled
and stroked her yellow
shalwar khameez
so butterly
and buttercuply
that all our fingers turned yellow.

snollygoster

Snollygoster
you told me, "If you give me your KitKat
I won't let Jake Harris kick you,"

Snollygoster
you said, "Don't leave your custard
or the dinner lady'll get you,"

Snollygoster
you took my new felt-tip pens
then helped me look for them,

Snollygoster
you pushed me under
when no one was looking,
then you said, "I was only trying
to teach you how to swim,"

Snollygoster
Snollygoster
I didn't tell my mum
I didn't tell anyone,

but, Snollygoster,
I told myself:
You don't need that Snollygoster
you don't need that felt-tip-stealing
push-you-under
eat-that-custard
no-kick-for-a-KitKat
best friend
Snollygoster.

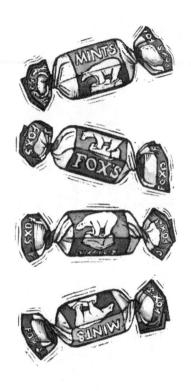

reading to my friend Miss Cross

Miss Cross next door
is thin as paper
and the wind aches her.
After school I read to her.

"Tuck my shawl in tight," she tells me.
We suck Fox's Glacier Mints,
drink our tea, then begin
on the front page with the headlines.

"Well", she says, "would you believe it?
Such wickedness!" Then I turn
the pages and read the horoscope
and tonight's TV programmes.

It's hard work, reading
all the big words and long columns
but Miss Cross says
the way I read, she can just see it.

Miss Cross wears a woolly hat
indoors, to keep her head warm.
She wraps her scarf around her
like a snowman in the garden.

She is thin as paper
and her bones ache her,
but we tuck her shawl in tight
and she says when I'm reading to her
she always feels warm.

strip

He's got it.
It cost a lot,
weeks of waiting and saving up,
Mum paying half and the rest
part of his Christmas present.

He's put it on
in the bedroom
for the very first time,
he's gone downstairs looking like everything
he ever wanted. Shining.

He's playing
better than ever,
he'll get picked for the team
if he keeps this up. Weeks
of wearing the strip,
Mum grabbing it off him to wash it.

One day out shopping
in town with Mum
he's into extra time
with the crowd roaring him on.
Two big boys shove ahead of him.

They're laughing.
Look at that idiot.
Doesn't he know they've got a new strip?

pearlie mountblossom

Pearlie Mountblossom's lost her mother
she lives in a tent with her dad and her brother,
the wind blew out and the sea blew in
and Pearlie early learned to swim,

Pearlie dreams in her tent at night
that the sails are set and the stars are bright
and the waves are turning over and over
and they show the face of Pearlie's mother,

Pearlie Mountblossom has forty pounds,
she keeps it safe in a hole in the ground,
her leggings have stars on, her dreams are sweet
though her brother is snoring down at her feet,

Pearlie Mountblossom grows mustard seeds,
she keeps her flowerpots clean of weeds,
her mustard blows in the morning wind
while Pearlie's father shaves and sings,

Pearlie has friends but they never come home,
her brother plays but he plays alone,
her dad splits kindling to make the fire
and the flames leap higher and higher and higher,

Pearlie Mountblossom's lost her mother,
she lives in a tent with her dad and her brother,
she has apples for breakfast and Mars bars for tea
and at night she sails the whispering sea.

pearl and the mushrooms

It was early, so early
it was time before sun
in the cool dawn

Pearl was alone
where anything might come,
where her breath came quick,
where the cattle trod
slowly, ripping the grass,
champing it in
between their teeth,
green wad
dropping long ropes of spit.

They were calm.
No flies troubled them
nobody came
but mist and mushrooms
and Pearl picking them,
picking the mushrooms
stripping their skin.
If it peeled
to white satin
Pearl knew they were safe to eat.

Pearl got up early
and found the mushrooms
before anyone touched them.
Pearl cycled alone
and found the morning
before anyone saw it.

fudge

Fat as a cloud
and paler than toffee,
marked with a swirl
like cream in coffee,
apple addict, carrot muncher,
sawdust sleeper, midnight walker,

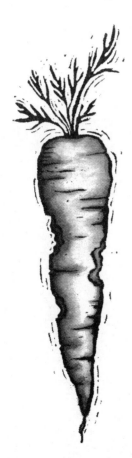

squeak of a wheel in the heart of the night,
creak of a cage-door that swings in the moonlight.

Who made holes in my duvet cover?
Who chewed through the phone wires?
Who stole Polos from my brother
and wheeled them under the gas-fire?

Patter of claws on the kitchen work-surface
whisper of whiskers searching the fridge,

nut-nibbler, cornflake cruncher,
apple addict, carrot muncher,

cool as cream
stirred into coffee,
down cracks in floorboards
he stretches like toffee,
food fiend, freedom finder,
fear-nothing feast forager,
nut nobbler, night nibbler,
fat as a ball of butter –
Fudge.

harbour seal

Come with the slop of tide up the slipway
come when we're not looking, come suddenly
cutting salt water like butter and
making a ballet of catching
the fishermen's litter,

come while we eat our ice creams and chatter
and make the glow of it happen
from a flash of recognition,
laugh at us as your nostrils close
in your wet black nose,

come for the French student on exchange
flipping the dictionary for your name
saying "Seal!" to her friend,
and for the child looking at you
wondering what it's like to be you –

come with your fat wet sides shining
cutting salt water like butter and
making a ballet of catching
our hearts' litter,
and then
go freely again.

baby orang-utan

Bold flare of orange –
a struck match
against his mother's breast

he listens to her heartbeat
going yes yes yes

21

richard the bad, richard the good

Richard the Bad was a Staffordshire bull terrier with eyes like wildfire. Richard was a warrior.

If he spotted a poodle or dachshund or tyke
he was after it before you could say knife.

He ought to be locked up, muzzled and chained,
If you set him free he'd only do it again.

Richard the Good was a Staffordshire bull terrier:
my mother's dog, a bit of a worrier

after dark if she was late home.
He never liked her going out alone,

but with him my mother
had the freedom of Manchester,
no park was too dark for her
and her Staffordshire bull terrier.

piglets

skin tight pink
sausages frisking
in first flick of sun

their Mum
chomping
on swedes
wanting
to eat
the world

25

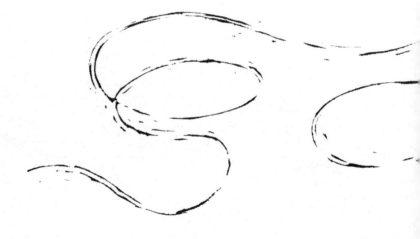

the perfect pet

Some think a tarant
ula's exotic,
it's not, it's
just something to make your parents frant
ic.

Forget
those fair-weather pets.
Slugs may be ug
ly but your snug
gly rabbit or hamster
(or even tarantula)
won't come out when it's wet.

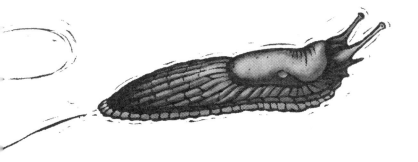

27

russian doll

When I held you up to my cheek you were cold
when I came close to your smile it dissolved,

the paint on your lips was as deep
as the steaming ruby of beetroot soup

but your breath smelled of varnish and pine
and your eyes swivelled away from mine.

When I wanted to open you up
you glowed, dumpy and perfect

smoothing your dozen little selves
like rolls of fat under your apron

and I hadn't the heart to look at them.
I knew I would be spoiling something.

But when I listened to your heart
I heard the worlds inside of you spinning
like the earth on its axis spinning.

the bear in the hall

Dear Grandma
thanks a million for the camera.
Christmas was brilliant
but

when you go upstairs in our house
when you go downstairs in our house
when you open the front door
when you close the front door
when you open any other kind of door
he's there
the bear in the hall.

He doesn't do anything
he doesn't say anything
he doesn't even eat anything
but

he's eight foot tall
his claws are steel
you should see the size of his teeth
you should hear the noise of his breath.

We go to bed
we sleep all night
we brush our teeth
we fight

but
when we get up

he's waiting,
quite still
the bear in the hall.
His fur is as thick as night
and his eyes frighten
everyone
even Mum.

We can't go upstairs
we can't go downstairs
we can't open the front door
we can't close the front door
we can't open any other door

without seeing him there
the bear in the hall.

Dear Grandma
can you come
and tell the bear in the hall
that none of us wants him at all,
not even Mum.
Please come.

the butcher's daughter

Where have you been, my little daughter
out in the wild weather?

I have met with a sailor, mother,
he has given me five clubs for juggling
and says I must go with him for ever.

Oh no, my treasure
you must come in and stay for ever
for you are the butcher's daughter.

Where have you been, my little daughter
in the winter weather?

I have met a man of war, mother,
he has given me four hoops to dance through
and he says I must love him for ever.

Oh no, my treasure
you must come in and shut the door
for you are the butcher's daughter.

Where have you been, my little daughter,
out in stormy weather?

I have met with a prince, mother,
and he has given me three promises
and I must rule his heart for ever.

Oh no, my treasure
you must give back his promises
for you are the butcher's daughter.

Where have you been, my little daughter
in the wild of the weather?

I have spoken to a wise man, mother,
who gave me knowledge of good and evil
and said I must learn from him for ever.

Oh no, my treasure
you have no need of his knowledge
for you are the butcher's daughter.

Where have you been, my little daughter
out in the summer weather?

I have met with a butcher, mother,
and he is sharpening a knife for me
for I am the butcher's daughter.

light as a leaf

Her boat was light as a leaf on her back
as she carried it to the shoreline,

there was grey rising behind the huts –
she'd timed it well, it was dawn.

Her boat was light as a leaf
as she sat, chin on her knees

and the cold tide started to pull
at the frame of her coracle.

She was quick and neat as a fish
as she paddled away out of it,

out of the smoke and the dogs barking,
and a winter of old people dying.

Her boat span like a leaf
in the rip-tide by the rocks

so by the time the sun came up
she and her coracle were a dot

as she sailed off somewhere
the story can't follow her.

what shall I draw?

Draw a house with four walls
a white fence with a gate in it
four windows, a smoking chimney –
and the path must be lined
with cockleshells and sunflowers.

What shall I draw next?

An apple tree and a plum tree
a sheet of grass, pale green,
a tent made from a blanket,
washing on the washing-line.

What shall I put in the house?

A face at the window looking out,
four chairs, a table, a bowl of fruit
and in the room with the red curtains
you can draw yourself, sleeping.

You can draw yourself, sleeping.
Even when the doors are shut
you can draw your way home.

little horse in the wardrobe

Tap of hooves like clothes-hangers chiming
then a whinny that might be
the shut-down of the central heating

or a horse calling to me,
the chink of its harness like coins
loose in my jeans.

Little horse, I whisper
and he answers
with the smart spark of his metal shoes.

This is a bad place for you
all big buildings and cars
nowhere you can put down your head
and eat grass.

Stay where you are,
I whisper. It's better
for you in the dark where

your eyes shine bright
as you make pictures of what might
be waiting for
little horses
out here.

wolf in my pocket

The wolf in my pocket is hungry
because he can't hunt by the moon,
because the winter snow has melted without him,
because the stitching of the sun
on pine tree shadow
is far away, but unforgotten.

The wolf in my pocket is angry,
beating a path where the zip
rasps but never opens,
he lollops up and down the lining
catching fluffballs in his claws –
his grey fur is too warm.

The wolf in my pocket howls
as he turns by the seam,
once he had cubs and a cave for them,
now he has none,
once he was cold and alive
on dangerous nights
but now he sleeps and his tongue
hangs out for nothing.

hedgehog hiding at harvest in
hills above monmouth

Where you hide
    moon-striped grass ripples like tiger skin
where you hide
    the dry ditch rustles with crickets,

where you hide
    the electricity pylon hums and sighs
    and the combine harvester's headlight
    pierces the hedges,

where you hide
    in your ball of silence
    your snorts muffled
    your squeaks and scuffles
    gone dumb,

    a foggy moon sails over your head,
    the stars are nipped in the bud,

where you hide
    you hear the white-faced owl hunting
    you count the teeth of the fox.

the moon's jigsaw

Take the invisible half of the moon's jigsaw,
or the marks you didn't get out of ten,

take the pounds lost on diets
which nobody's found yet,

take the unused miles on the speedometer
because no one ever goes that fast

or those seconds that tick tick TOCK
after you've hung up on the Speaking Clock.

Leftovers. Breaktimes when nothing happens
because you fell out with your friend,

the birthday present half-saved-for,
the card you never remembered to send,

the hidden stripes of a zebra at night,
the invisible half of the moon's jigsaw –

what are they waiting for?

country darkness

Now is its time.
Quiet as a vixen,
happiest under the trees
in its own rustling,
country darkness is coming.

Country darkness is coming.
Stand on a wall
high above town in the cold
and watch it fall.
Now is its time.

Country darkness is coming.
It was waiting all the time,
smelling of frost and leaves
with night up its sleeves,
now is its time.

Watch it wrapping up nightclubs
in velvety sleep,
watch it stopping
the late-night shopping,
watch it pinch out party-goers'
glittering clothes,
watch it stride into town.
Country darkness is coming,
now is its time.

night cat

She's there by the fence
but you mustn't call out,
like a scoop of night
or a water shadow
tense for flight
she'll twist and go,
don't open your mouth –
the moon's so close
that the stars blow out –
leaving that patch
where the moon shone
leaving the empty
dress of night
with the stars picked out
and you alone.

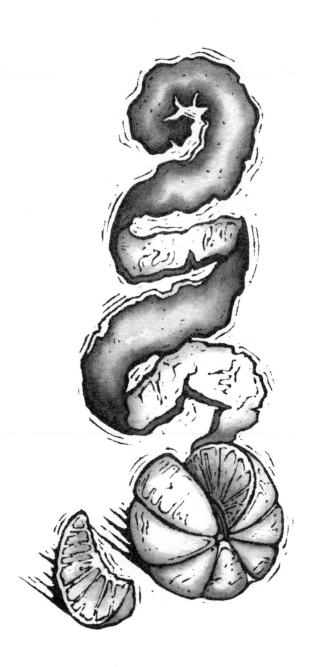

mid-winter haiku

Ice on the windows,
tangerines peeled in one curl
under the duvet.

Christmas in prison,
barbed wire glitters in searchlights –
a fence made of stars.

Two plastic reindeer,
a shopping bag of holly
a mouthful of frost.

The houses are shut,
no one walks the empty streets –
has there been a death?

Chocolate fever –
we dig for gold-wrapped treasure
deep in our stockings.

the light in the stable

There's paper snow on our windows
and thirty-six toilet roll angels
that dance when the door opens

There's a sharp silver star
and a fat red-painted postbox
that eats all our Christmas cards,

and a junk-model grotto
for Father Christmas and his reindeer
with cotton-wool snow.

But what I like is the little light
that switches on in the stable
so we can see the baby.

And today, just before home-time,
after the story, Miss told me
Come on, it's your turn.
And I switched it on.

snollygoster

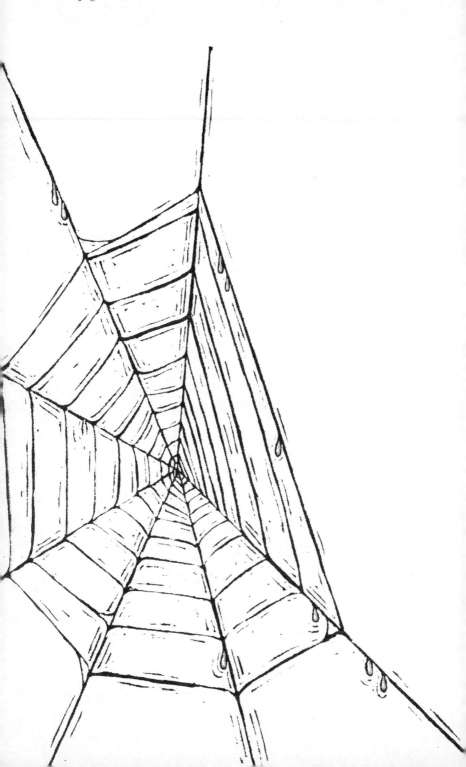

for francesca

it's so early in the morning

the cobweb
stretched between the gateposts
is not yet broken

couples
stir in their beds
and sigh and smile
and the hard
words of the day
are not yet spoken

it's so early in the morning

the street lamps go out
one by one
the small stars disappear
and your life
has barely begun

it's so early in the morning

playground haiku

Everyone says our
playground is overcrowded
but I feel lonely

put your hand up

Please Miss, I want to go to the –
　　Don't call out, Jack
　　Put your hand up!

Please Miss, I don't know where my –
　　That's enough shouting Salim
　　Put your hand up!

Please Miss, Darren's talking –
　　Hannah, I've told you a hundred times
　　Put your hand up!

Please Miss, my mum's given me crocodile
                              sandwiches again –
    Jason, do you want to stay in at playtime?
    Put your hand up!

Please Miss, Mr Boardman's grown wings,
I saw him flying past the window,
and Class One spent all their dinner money
on sherbet fountains, and Tracey Kingston's mum
says she's coming in to teach tap-dancing
instead of hearing our reading,
and there's a baby dinosaur on the wildlife table –

    Justine! I will not have this chatter-chattering!
    What did I just say?
    Tell her, everyone!
    Put your hand up! Put your hand up!

(But what's that noise of wings flapping
 and tap-dancing and sweet-munching
 and dinosaur feet crunch-crunching?)

the other half of Miss

Home-time! –
so long time coming
the whole world's moved round.
My shadow's walking backwards.
Mum's got new gloves on.
There's a huge puddle jumping with shine
next to the bins.
Mum says Didn't you see the rain?
Miss looks small at the door
going back in.
My mum says to Nick's mum
Miss Riley's ever so good
she half lives up at the school.
I kick the puddle and it kicks back
and Mum pulls my arm.
As we walk home I wish
I could see the other half of Miss.

the braggart and the pudding

It came in the night.

Nobody saw it.
Nobody made it.

By dawn it was steaming
among the horse-mushrooms,
astonishing
the fog-damp sheep
and the children,

rolling and boiling
fruit-studded
spice-smoking
fuming and gleaming
glossily steaming
sugar sweet
citrus sharp
PUDDING

so big you could not wrap your arms around it
so big it would put out the fire in your kitchen
so big there would be enough for everyone.

"I'LL HAVE IT,"
said the Braggart
and put his boot on the pudding.

The people drew back
and laid their hands over the mouths
of the children,
and looking at the pudding
one by one
they muttered

"OK, you take it" "That's fine"
"think nothing of it" "you take it" "forget it"
"can't eat rich food anyway"
"haven't the stomach for it"
"good on you, Braggart" "you take it"

So the Braggart took it.
With his bare hands he took it
and raced off palming it
between his hands
with the steam slapping them

his red red hands
long and pointed as flames.

The Braggart took the world of the pudding
to his secret place

to his cave of bones

where he kept his knife
and his white spoon
made from a bull's thigh-bone.

So.
He rolls up his sleeves
braces his legs like a wrestler
snorting
he rocks forward
and so
he advances upon the pudding

> Oh the Braggart
> the great man
> he went to war
> upon a pudding

It was so delicious he could have wept
as his spoon oozed through the crust
and out came
a nestful of eggs
warm and brown
flour fine-milled as silk
a thin current of honey,

out came blackstrap molasses
ginger stem

and a full bottle
of brandy-wine.

It was so delicious he could have laughed
as he dug his way to the heart
of that marvellous pudding,
through mazes of grapes
through candied groves
of orange and lemon.

Time passed.
The sheep ate their way through the fog.
The people thought that one morning
the pudding would come again,
and the children listened.

Towards night they began to hear sounds
neither like weeping nor laughing.
Everyone fell silent.
Was it the Braggart?

It was the pudding
the marvellous pudding
the pudding speaking

rolling and boiling
fruity and fuming
stuck with cloves
and steaming with spices.

It spoke in a voice
as rough as the iron
pot it had boiled in:

"Come on! Come on!"
the pudding taunted
its bleary punch-drunk
belching opponent.
Eyes half-closed
the Braggart staggered
across the ring
squinting at nothing.

"Come on! Come on!"
taunted the pudding.

"There's your man!"
        the people whisper
        smelling the wind
        which is heavy with pudding.

The children hold hands

        and run on tiptoe

        as close as they dare

        to the secret place
        to the cave of bones

        where the pudding swells
        and the Braggart slumps

        holds up his hands
        and says "You win,"

        and the children laugh
        as loud as they dare

and the children yell
as loud as they can:
"YES! THERE'S YOUR MAN!"

the bones of the Vasa

(The VASA was a royal Swedish ship of the sixteenth century. She sank on her maiden voyage.)

I saw the bones of the Vasa knit in the moonlight
I heard her hull creak as the salt sea slapped it
I smelled her tar and her freshly-planed pine,

there were rye loaves slung up on poles for drying
there were herrings in barrels and brandy-wine
and every plank in her body was singing,

off-duty sailors were throwing the dice
while the royal flag cracked at the mast
and the wind grew strong and the clouds flew past.

Oh the Vasa never set sail down the salt sea's stream
down the salt stream for a second time
where the midsummer islands waited like secrets,

the King's Vasa flew down like a swan
parting the waves and the sea's furrow
parting that long road where the drowned roll
and the tide rules the kingdom of no one.

breeze of ghosts

Tall ship hanging out at the horizon
tall ship blistering the horizon
you've been there so long
your sheets and decks white
in the sun

what wind whispers you in?

Tall ship creaking at the horizon
your captain long gone
your crew in the cabin
drinking white rum
their breath spiralling

what wind breathes you in?

Tall ship tilting to the shoreline
past Spanish palms
tall ship coming in like a swan
in the mid-day sun

what wind blows you in?

It is the cool wind of the morning
stirring my masts
before the sun
burns it to nothing,
they call it
breeze of ghosts.

lorries behind

The teeth of lorries in the driving mirror
the breath of lorries on the rear window

the hiss of lorries waiting to shoulder by,
the throb of diesel, the air-brake sigh

the hot shimmer in the driving mirror.
Lorries behind. Too close. Look at that smile.

night lorries

unzipping miles
of white lane-lines
approaching
faster than owls

gap-toothed lorries
spangled like castles
round the black hole
of night cargoes

headlights full on
wheel-towers
drumming the crown
of the fast lane

and they're gone, making
that thin finishing whine

red lights
in your mirror
not even braking

snollygoster

sad lorries

Wayside sad lorries
jackknifed, slipshod

one wheel on the road
nobody's rig

halfway to the wrecker's

one wheel on the road
lorries lying low

two days
with small corrugate smiles

they wait for the crusher
to wipe out the miles

free-wheeling

I race downhill
through hoops of shadow
free-wheeling
tyres blazing.

I come down
slow as a yawn
in a mash of blood
on the tarred kerbstone,
my blood all new
on the yellow lines.

Heads hide the sun,
say I am bleeding.
I suck my lips
and I can't feel it,
my breath is quick
as feathers flying,
I hear the wheels
tick round and round,
I hear my bike
free-wheeling on.

the pelting rain

Poor Johnny
he's lost it again
he's out trying to find it
in the pelting rain

the wild woods are thrashing
the weather's insane
trees double over

jays scream for shelter
the lamppost flashes
signals for rescue

and Johnny'd better
skid helter-skelter
for safe haven

but he's gone again
poor Johnny
looking for sunshine
in the pelting rain.

four

On our first morning
Miss asked us how old we were.
She asked us one by one
and everyone
shone with knowing the answer –
"Miss! Miss! I'm four!"

But then some of them grew up
to five, like a club
I wanted to join
but they wouldn't let me in,

when we made our hats for Halloween
Peter and Richard and Nasreem
sat together on the fives table.

I'm the donkey in the stable
and the fives are Mary and Joseph
and the Angel Gabriel

I was sad in the home corner
thinking about being four
only four, always waiting
for five to begin,

I didn't want to go out at playtime
so I told my friend Jasmine
and she told Miss, and Miss came
and Miss asked why I was crying,

and I told her it's not fair
I can't stop being four.
Miss checked when my birthday was
and she told me it was fifty-three days.

Fifty-three days of being four!

But Miss said, Those days are like treasure
those days of being four
be four every day you can
every minute till it's gone.

It was still playtime
I was still four
four, like treasure,

and Miss gave me a sticker
and I stuck it on,
she says the words say
FOUR AND COUNTING .

all the voices have gone

All the voices have gone.
I sit up straight on the carpet
with my jacket zipped to the neck
waiting for Mum.

I hold my lunch box tight
and my bonfire painting.
Miss says, Right,
no point sitting there waiting.

I can do what I like.
I can build roads in the sand,
I can have the red digger all the time
and not take turns.

All the voices have gone.
The computer hums
and prints something for Miss
and I wait for Mum.

I sit up straight on the carpet
with my jacket zipped to the neck
while Miss works at her desk
and I watch the door for Mum.

If I shut my eyes then open them
she'll come.

the speak mum speaks

the speak Mum speaks
when she's on the phone
I asked her one time
where it comes from
she says it's the speak
of her friends from home

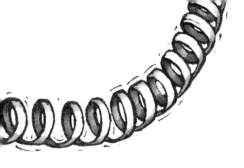

the speak Mum speaks
like floating and laughing
and the words are bubbling
whispering hurrying
she says it's the speak
of where she comes from

the speak Mum speaks
like singing and dancing
like friends holding hands
going out to playtime
like a playground
with everyone jumping

I sit small and say nothing
I listen and listen
to the speak Mum speaks
flashing and shining
like jewel diamonds
and I want some

89